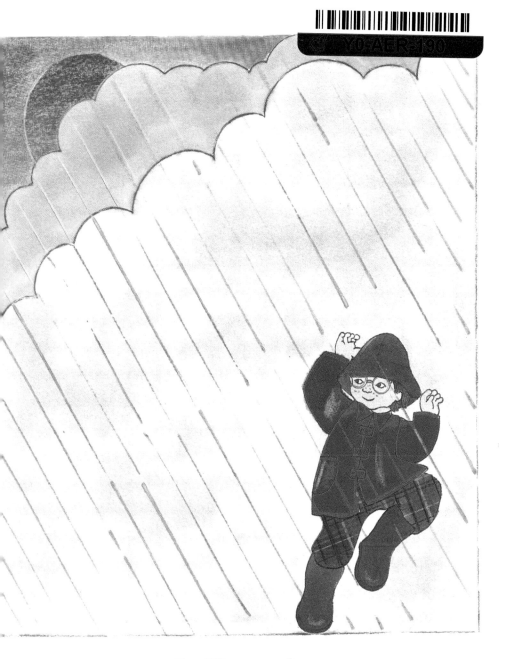

I like rain.

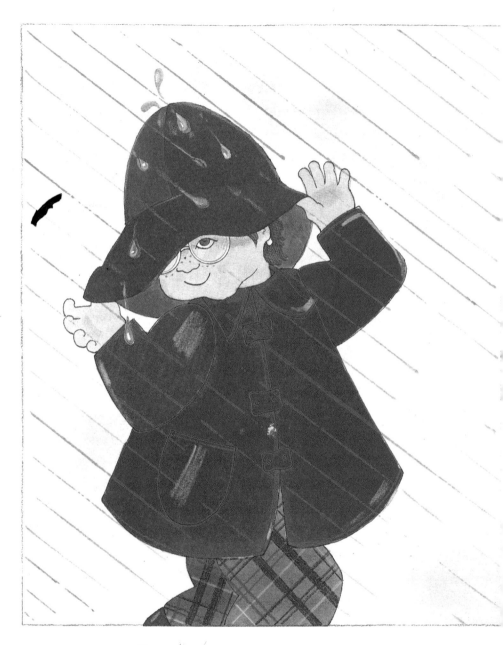

It falls on my hat.

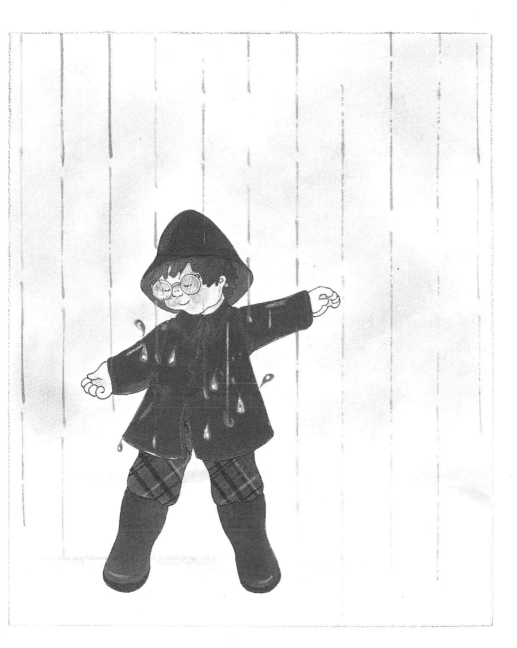

It falls on my coat.

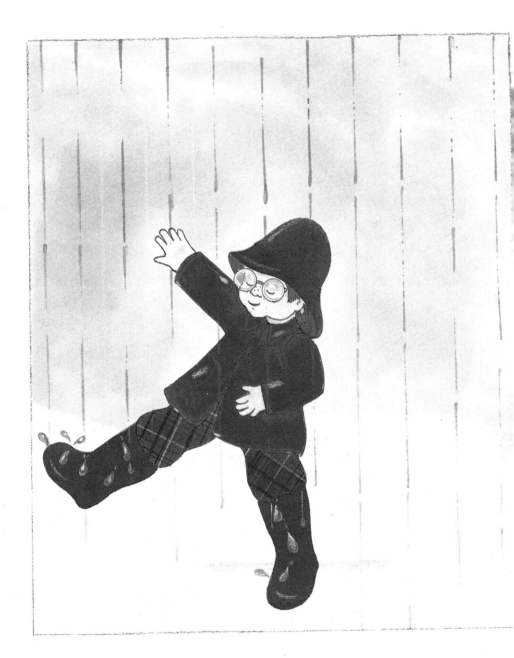

It falls on my boots.

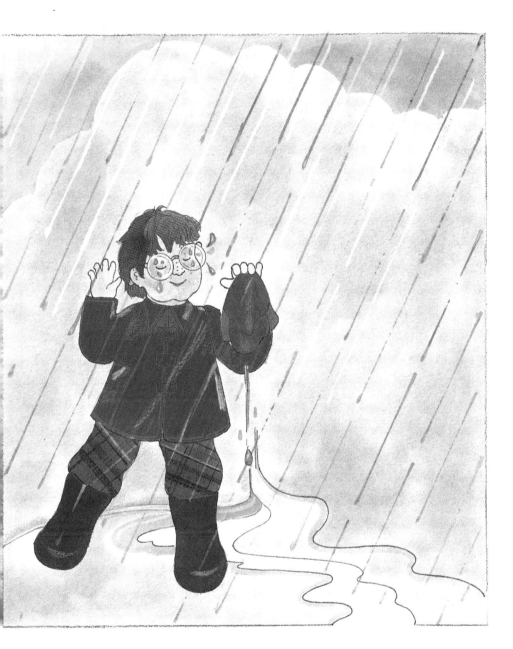

It falls on my glasses.

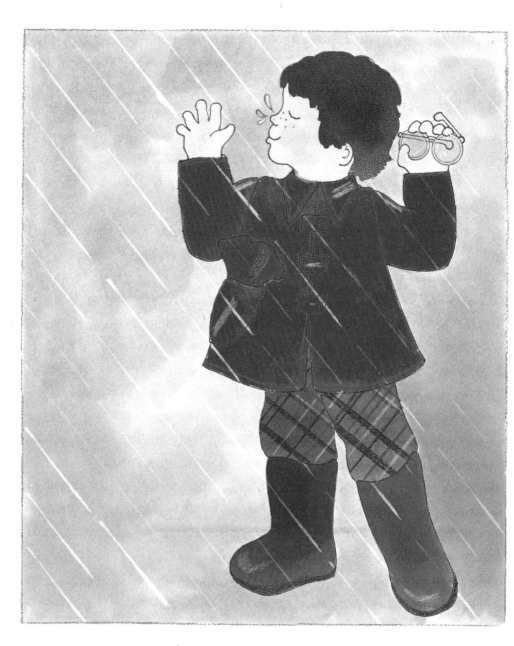

It falls on my nose.

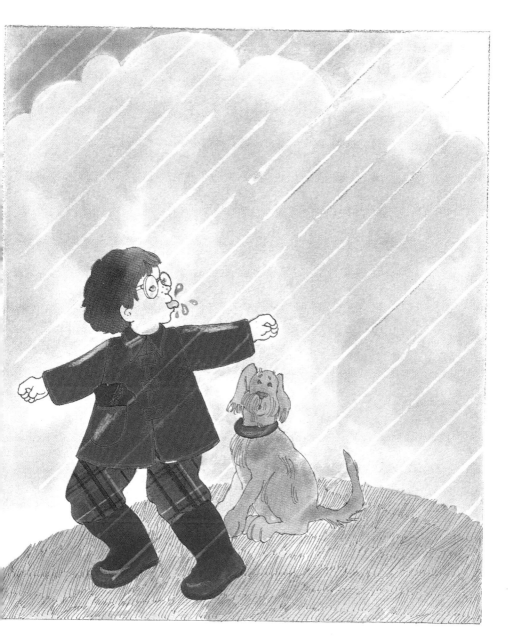

It falls on my tongue.

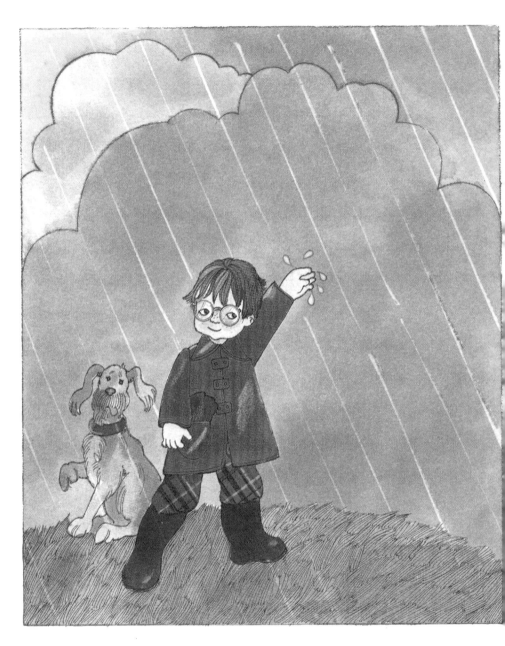

It falls on my hand.

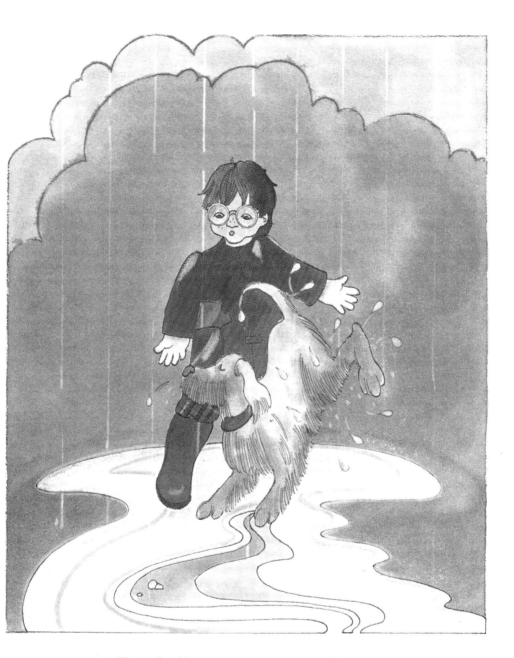

It falls on my dog.

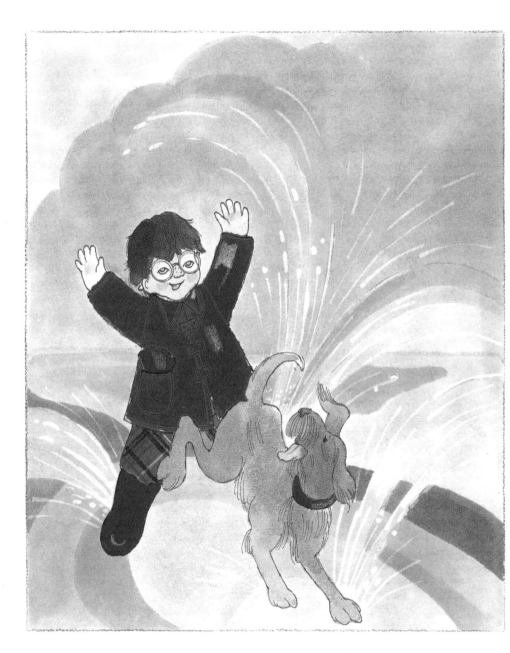

It makes puddles.

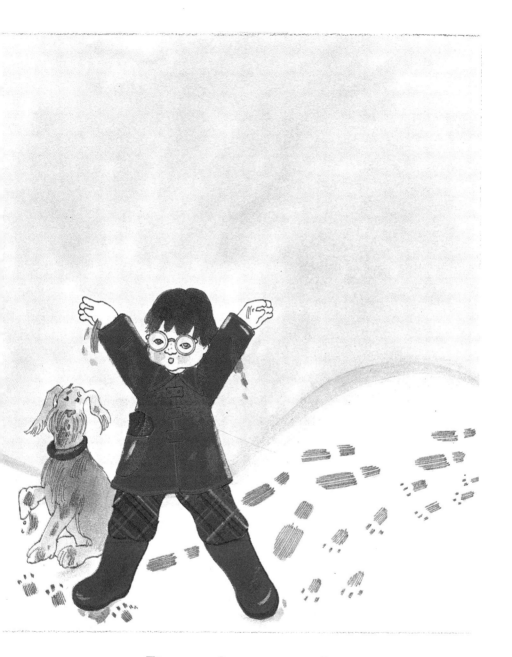

It makes mud.

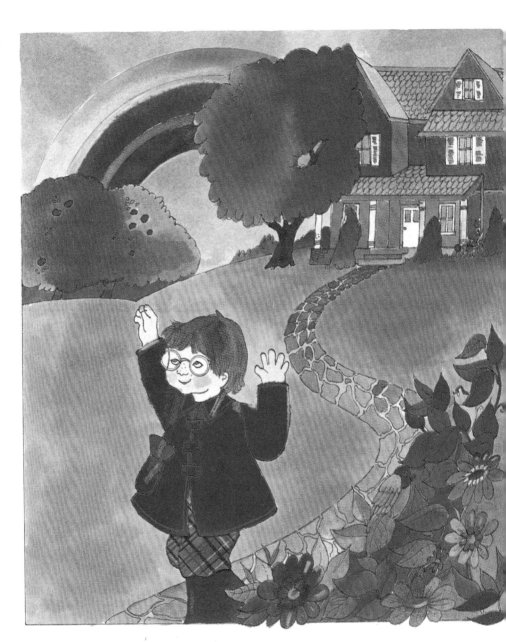

It makes rainbows.